A Banker's Busy Day

Written and Illustrated by Read With You
Center for Excellence in STEAM Education

Read With You

Published by Read With You Publishing. Printed in the United States of America.

Read With You and associated logos are trademarks and/or registered trademarks of Read With You L.L.C.

ISBN-13: 979-8-88618-327-6

First Edition January 2023

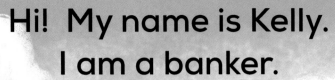

Hi! My name is Kelly.
I am a banker.

I work at a bank. I count money and keep it safe.

One day, Mr. Penguin walks in. "How can I help you?" I ask.

"I want to make a deposit,"
Mr. Penguin says.
"Of how much?" I ask.

"All of these,"
Mr. Penguin says.
Oh, dear! These will take me
all day to count.

One... two... three...
"Excuse me!" Mrs. Hippo says.
"I need to make a withdrawal."

"Of how much?" I ask.
"One quarter," she says.

"Only one quarter?" I ask, scratching my head. "Here you go."

"Thank you!" Mrs. Hippo says. "Now, I can play heads-or-tails."

I go back to counting coins. Where was I? Four... five... six...

11

"Excuse me!" says Mr. Rabbit.
"I need change for one dollar."

"Here are four quarters," I say.
"I don't want quarters," Mr.
Rabbit says.

"Here are ten dimes," I say.
"I don't want dimes," he says.

"Twenty nickels?" I ask.
"No, thank you," he says.

"Do you want one hundred pennies?" I ask.

"Perfect!" says Mr. Rabbit.
"One for each of my bunnies!"

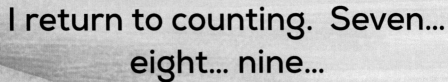

I return to counting. Seven... eight... nine...

"Excuse me!" Pudgy Panda says. "Give me one million dollars!"

"Are you making a withdrawal?" I ask.

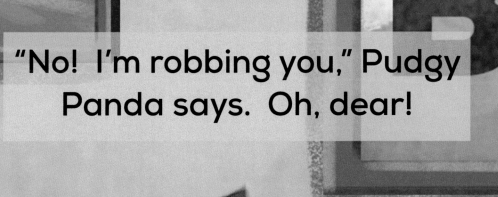

"No! I'm robbing you," Pudgy Panda says. Oh, dear!

I have an idea! I give Pudgy Panda Mr. Penguin's coins.

"Is this one million dollars?"
Pudgy Panda asks.
"I don't know," I say. "You
must count it."

"One... two... three..."
While Pudgy Panda counts, I
contact the police.

When the police come, Pudgy is still counting.
"Nine hundred and ninety-nine..."

"Stop!" the police say.
"Hands up!"
"Oh, no!" Pudgy says.
"I've been tricked."

Hooray! I am a hero!
"Are you finished with my
deposit yet?" Mr. Penguin
asks.

I sigh.
Back to counting...

Answer

- What does a banker do?

- Which character takes money from Kelly?

- Which characters give money to Kelly?

- How does Kelly save the day at the end of the book?

Learn

This book is filled with words related to being a **banker**! Look at the list below. Do you know what these words mean?

- banker
- bank
- withdrawal
- deposit
- quarter
- dime

Can you think of any other words related to being a banker? Think about different words for money!

Act

Piggy banks are a great way to save money. Do you have a piggy bank? If you do, make a goal for how much you'd like to save in your piggy bank over the next month. If you don't have a piggy bank, make one by asking an adult to help you cut a slit into the top of an empty water bottle. Decorate the water bottle, then start adding money in through the slit! How much can you save?

Discover

Why are banks important? Imagine that banks did not exist. Where would people keep their money? How would they keep their money safe?

Made in the USA
Coppell, TX
17 April 2023

15689170R10021